THIS IS A RECORD OF MY FIRST FIVE YEARS

Name

M·I·L·K ™

FRIENDSHIP
FAMILY
LOVE
& LAUGHTER

Baby
Record Book
MY FIRST FIVE YEARS

WPL

www.wpl.eu.com

in association with PQ Blackwell

Every baby born into the world
is a finer one than the last.

Contents

Before you were conceived I wanted you.

Before you were born I loved you.

Before you were here an hour I would die for you.

This is the miracle of life.

My story begins

MY DUE DATE IS

_____

BEFORE I WAS BORN MY PARENTS CALLED ME

_____

_____

_____

WHEN THEY WERE EXPECTING ME MY PARENTS FELT

_____

_____

_____

_____

WHAT MY PARENTS WERE DOING WHEN MY MOTHER WENT INTO LABOUR

_____

_____

_____

A baby makes love stronger, days shorter, nights longer, bank balance smaller, home happier, clothes shabbier, the past forgotten, and the future worth living for.

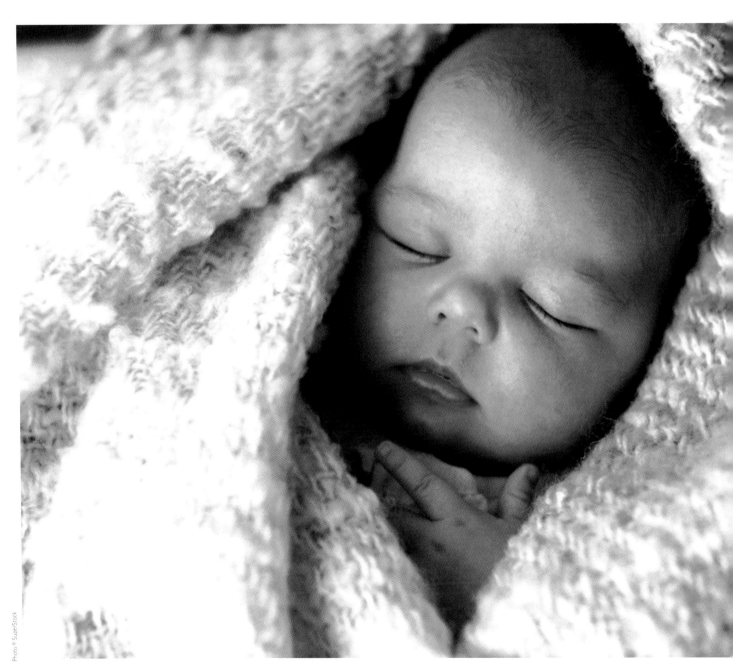

The day I was born

DATE

TIME

DAY OF WEEK

LENGTH OF LABOUR

LOCATION / HOSPITAL

MEDICAL TEAM

SUPPORT CREW

SPECIAL MEMORIES

your photo here

your photo here

your photo here

your photo here

Photographs

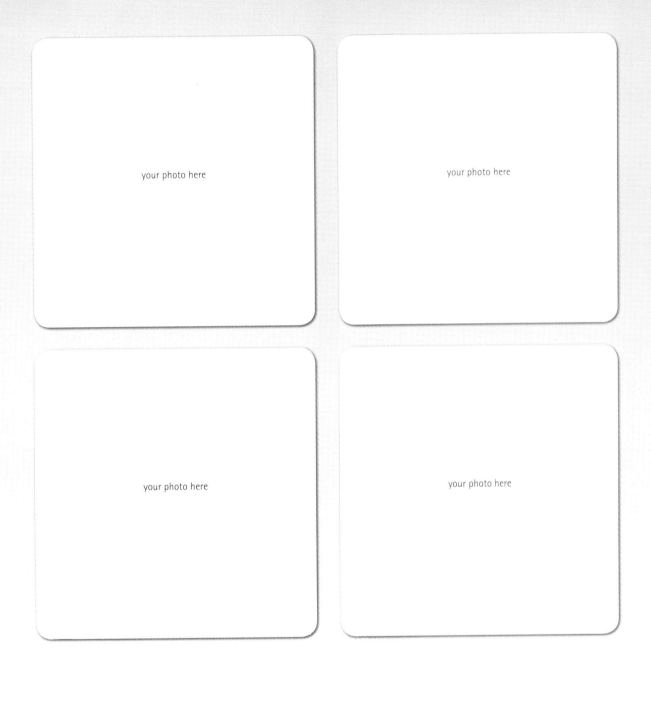

There are not seven wonders of the world in the eyes of a child – there are seven million.

First appearances

MY WEIGHT

MY LENGTH

MY HAIR COLOUR

MY FIRST MOMENTS WITH MY PARENTS

A LOCK OF MY

BABY HAIR

Babies are such a nice way to start people.

My name

MY NAME IS

MY PARENTS CHOSE IT BECAUSE

MY NICKNAME/S ARE

BECAUSE

OTHER NAMES MY PARENTS CONSIDERED WERE

MY NAMING CEREMONY

PERFORMED BY

MY CEREMONY WAS

MY PARENTS' FAVOURITE MEMORY OF THE DAY

your photo here

your photo here

your photo here

your photo here

Photographs

your photo here

your photo here

your photo here

your photo here

Seek the wisdom of the ages, but look at
the world through the eyes of a child.

What was happening in the world

THE NUMBER-ONE SONG

THE NUMBER-ONE FILM

A CINEMA FILM TICKET COST

ONE LITRE OF MILK COST

THE NEWS STORIES OF THE DAY

IMPORTANT LEADERS AROUND THE WORLD

There is no friendship,
no love like that of a parent for their child.

Coming home

MY PARENTS FELT
_____

_____

I WENT HOME ON
_____

THE CAR I RODE IN WAS
_____

MY FIRST HOME WAS AT
_____

FAMILY AND FRIENDS THERE TO WELCOME ME
_____

_____

WHERE I FIRST SLEPT
_____

I SLEPT FOR   HOURS
_____

your photo here

your photo here

Family faces are magic mirrors.
Looking at people who belong to us,
we see the past, present and future.

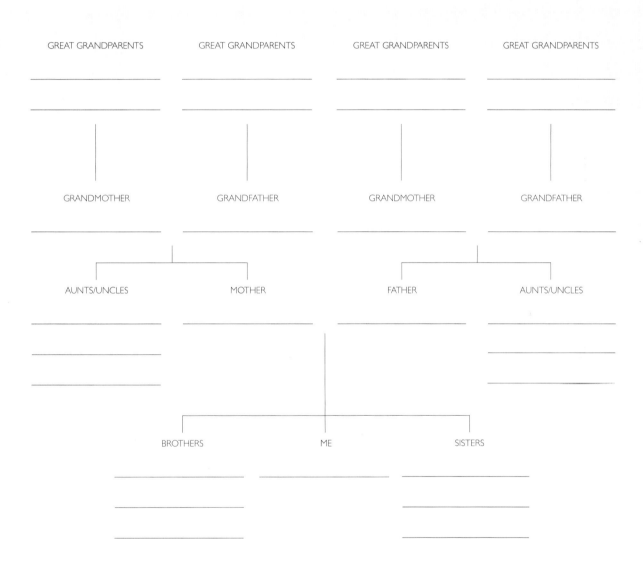

GREAT GRANDPARENTS   GREAT GRANDPARENTS   GREAT GRANDPARENTS   GREAT GRANDPARENTS

GRANDMOTHER   GRANDFATHER   GRANDMOTHER   GRANDFATHER

AUNTS/UNCLES   MOTHER   FATHER   AUNTS/UNCLES

BROTHERS   ME   SISTERS

your photo here

your photo here

your photo here

your photo here

Friends & loved ones

your photo here

your photo here

your photo here

your photo here

People who say they sleep like a baby don't usually have one.

Sleeping

IN THE BEGINNING

BEDTIME RITUALS

LULLABIES I LOVE

MY CUTEST SLEEPING HABIT

		AGE	DATE
IMPORTANT DATES	SLEEPING IN A COT		
	SLEEPING IN A BED		

MY FAVOURITE BEDTIME TOY/S

Picture

There are three reasons for breast-feeding :
the milk is always at the right temperature;
it comes in attractive containers; and the cat can't get it.

Eating

MY APPETITE

FOODS I LIKE

FOODS I DISLIKE

	AGE	DATE

WEANED FROM BREAST/BOTTLE

MY FIRST TOOTH

EATING SOLID FOOD

SITTING IN A HIGH CHAIR

DRINKING FROM A CUP

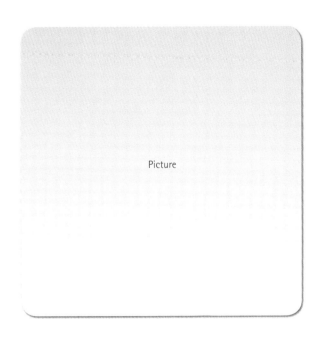

Picture

A baby is an angel whose wings decrease as his legs increase.

M·I·L·K

SITTING UP

AGE _____

DATE _____

CRAWLING

AGE _____

DATE _____

WAVING BYE-BYE

AGE _____

DATE _____

STANDING UP

AGE _____

DATE _____

MY FIRST STEPS

AGE _____

DATE _____

FIRST PAIR OF SHOES

AGE _____

DATE _____

your photo here

your photo here

your photo here

your photo here

Photographs

your photo here

your photo here

your photo here

your photo here

Having a child is surely the most beautifully irrational act that two people in love can commit.

Talking

MY FIRST WORDS

_____

_____

_____

_____

_____

MY FAVOURITE SAYING

_____

_____

_____

_____

_____

MY FAVOURITE SONG

_____

_____

_____

_____

_____

		AGE	DATE
IMPORTANT DATES	COUNTING TO TEN		
	SINGING THE ALPHABET		

What is a home without children? Quiet.

Laughing & crying

THINGS THAT MAKE ME HAPPY

WHEN I WAS HAPPY

your photo here

THINGS THAT MAKE ME SAD

WHEN I WAS SAD

your photo here

HOW MY PARENTS COMFORT ME

Never underestimate a child's
ability to get into more trouble.

Bath time & waterplay

MY FEELINGS ABOUT BATH TIME

_____

_____

_____

MY FAVOURITE BATH TOY/S

_____

_____

_____

_____

WATER GAMES I LOVE

_____

_____

_____

your photo here

your photo here

If you can give your child only one gift,

let it be enthusiasm.

My favourite things

GAMES
_____
_____
_____
_____

TOYS
_____
_____
_____

BOOKS
_____
_____

CLOTHES
_____
_____
_____

ACTIVITIES
_____
_____
_____

PLACES
_____
_____
_____
_____

DRESS-UPS
_____
_____
_____

TELEVISION CHARACTERS
_____
_____
_____

COLOURS

If you want your children to turn out well,
spend twice as much time with them
and half as much money on them.

Holidays & travel

MY FIRST HOLIDAY

_____

_____

DATE WHEN WE WENT

_____

_____

_____

WHO WENT WITH ME

_____

_____

_____

WHAT WE DID

_____

_____

_____

_____

_____

_____

_____

your photo here

your photo here

your photo here

your photo here

Photographs

your photo here

your photo here

your photo here

your photo here

A baby is an alimentary canal with a big appetite
at one end and no sense of responsibility at the other.

Celebrations & special occasions

DATE

EVENT

FAMILY AND FRIENDS WHO ATTENDED

DATE

EVENT

FAMILY AND FRIENDS WHO ATTENDED

We find delight in the beauty and happiness of
children that makes the heart too big for the body.

Caregivers

MY CAREGIVER/S NAMES

WHERE THEY LOOK AFTER ME

GAMES THEY PLAY WITH ME

Picture

The fundamental job of a toddler is to rule the universe.

My first year

MY FAVOURITE THINGS

GAMES

TOYS

BOOKS

ACTIVITIES

CLOTHES

COLOURS

TELEVISION CHARACTERS

PLACES

OTHER

GOING OUT

FUN PLACES WE VISIT

FAVOURITE OUTSIDE ACTIVITIES

SPECIAL OUTINGS WITH GRANDPARENTS/RELATIVES/FRIENDS AND PLAYMATES

Even when freshly washed and relieved of all
obvious confections, children tend to be sticky.

My second year

MY FAVOURITE THINGS

GAMES

TOYS

BOOKS

ACTIVITIES

CLOTHES

COLOURS

TELEVISION CHARACTERS

PLACES

OTHER

GOING OUT

FUN PLACES WE VISIT

FAVOURITE OUTSIDE ACTIVITIES

SPECIAL OUTINGS WITH GRANDPARENTS/RELATIVES/FRIENDS AND PLAYMATES

Mother nature is wonderful.

She gives us twelve years to develop a love for our children before turning them into teenagers.

My third year

MY FAVOURITE THINGS

GAMES

TOYS

BOOKS

ACTIVITIES

CLOTHES

COLOURS

TELEVISION CHARACTERS

PLACES

OTHER

GOING OUT

FUN PLACES WE VISIT

FAVOURITE OUTSIDE ACTIVITIES

SPECIAL OUTINGS WITH GRANDPARENTS/RELATIVES/FRIENDS AND PLAYMATES

The child supplies the power but the parents
have to do the steering.

My fourth year

MY FAVOURITE THINGS

GAMES

TOYS

BOOKS

ACTIVITIES

CLOTHES

COLOURS

TELEVISION CHARACTERS

PLACES

OTHER

GOING OUT

FUN PLACES WE VISIT

FAVOURITE OUTSIDE ACTIVITIES

SPECIAL OUTINGS WITH GRANDPARENTS/RELATIVES/FRIENDS AND PLAYMATES

If you want your children to keep their feet on the ground,
put some responsibility on their shoulders.

My fifth year

MY FAVOURITE THINGS

GAMES

TOYS

BOOKS

ACTIVITIES

CLOTHES

COLOURS

TELEVISION CHARACTERS

PLACES

OTHER

GOING OUT

FUN PLACES WE VISIT

FAVOURITE OUTSIDE ACTIVITIES

SPECIAL OUTINGS WITH GRANDPARENTS/RELATIVES/FRIENDS AND PLAYMATES

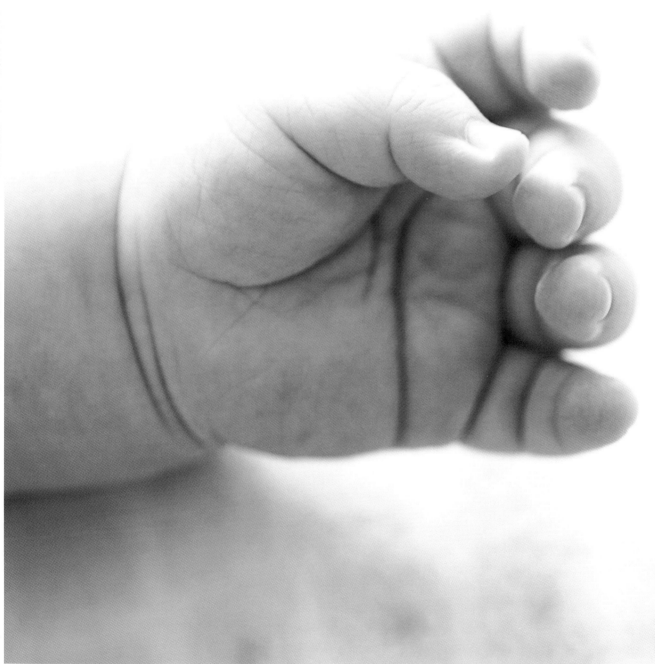

Hand & foot prints

IN THE BEGINNING

DATE _____

HAND

FOOT

Hand & foot prints

AT AGE FIVE

DATE _____

HAND

FOOT

Of all created things, the loveliest and most divine are children.

Growth

HEIGHT

BORN

3MTHS

6MTHS

9MTHS

1YR

2 YR

3YR

4YR

5YR

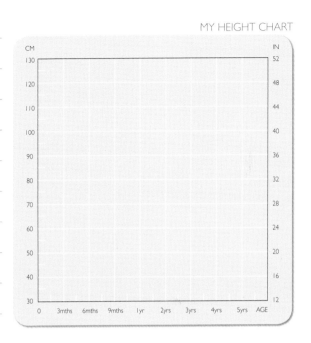

WEIGHT

BORN

3MTHS

6MTHS

9MTHS

1YR

2 YR

3YR

4YR

5YR

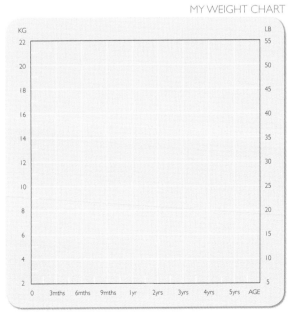

Each day of our lives we make deposits in
the memory banks of our children.

My parents' special message for me

DATE

www.wpl.eu.com

The Perfume Factory
140 Wales Farm Road
London, W3 6UG, UK

ISBN : 978-1-907667-81-7
This edition published in 2012 by WPL. www.wpl.eu.com

Printed in China.

M.I.L.K IMAGES

The photographer's four-month-old daughter, Olivia, is cuddled by her mother, Maeve.
© Nico Sepe

Photographed in Bristol, UK, the photographer's wife sees their two-minute-old son, Louie, for the first time.
© David White

Ensconced in her bucket, four-mouth-old Indigo supervises the washing being hung out in her backyard at Maroubra Beach, New South wales, Australia.
© Tanya Lake

In Nederhemert, Netherlands, eighteen-month-old Rijik, the photographer's second-born son, is engrossed in front of a computer, watching sesame street.
© Edward van Herk

In St Joseph's Hospital in Hamilton, Ontario, Canada, the photographer's son, Chris, holds his own son, Seth. Born prematurely, this is the first time Seth has been cuddled by his dad.
© John Marechal

In Sydney, Australia, the photographer's daughter, Danielle, is ready to be breastfed.
© Reg Morrison

One-year-old Grace shows off her crawling prowess to her mother, Jamie, in their home in Indianapolis, Indiana, USA.
© Anne Anderson

Mother, father and six-month-old son share an intimate moment in Kelowna, British Columbia, Canada.
© Tara Morris

Cousins Justin, Hanna and Austin find it too close for comfort in the tub in the photographers studio.
© Brandy Torvinen

Guests Ivy, Sarah and baby Harry, are captured at a wedding in Wiltshire, UK.
© Paul O'Connor

Jack and Jed are photographed at Jack's house in Houghton, Michigan, USA.
© Brandy Torvinen

Two young friends in Haarlem, Netherlands, hide from the photographer.
© Marcel Bakker

In Philadelphia, Pennsylvania, USA, young cousin set off down one of the City's old cobblestoned streets on their way to the playground.
© Joyce Smith

Siblings Milas and Maren are photographed together in West Plains, Missouri, USA.
© Lindsey Thompson

At the top of a lighthouse on Awhitu Peninsula, New Zealand, Kirby shelters his daughter, Elizabeth, from the elements.
© Heidi Coppock Beard